THE ARTS OF ASIA

**ASIAN ART MUSEUM
CHONG-MOON LEE CENTER
FOR ASIAN ART AND CULTURE**

2007 ENGAGEMENT CALENDAR

Pomegranate

Catalog No. V210
Published by Pomegranate Communications, Inc.
Box 808022, Petaluma CA 94975

© 2006 Asian Art Museum/Chong-Moon Lee Center for Asian Art and Culture

Available in Canada from Canadian Manda Group
165 Dufferin Street, Toronto, Ontario M6K 3H6

Available in the UK and mainland Europe from Pomegranate Europe Ltd.
Unit 1, Heathcote Business Centre, Hurlbutt Road, Warwick, Warwickshire CV34 6TD, UK

Available in Australia from Hardie Grant Books, 12 Claremont Street, South Yarra, Victoria 3141

Available in New Zealand from Southern Publishers Group, P.O. Box 8360, Symonds Street, Auckland

Available in the Far East from Julian Ashton, Ashton International Marketing Services
P.O. Box 298, Sevenoaks, Kent TN13 1WU, UK

Africa, Latin America, and the Middle East: info@pomegranate.com; 707-782-9000

Pomegranate also publishes the 2007 calendars *Hokusai; Domains of Wonder: Paintings from India; Hiroshige; Buddhist Paintings;* and *Japanese Scrolls and Screen Paintings,* as well as many other calendars in several formats. Our products and publications include books, posters, postcards and books of postcards, notecards and boxed notecard sets, magnets, mousepads, Knowledge Cards®, birthday books, journals, address books, jigsaw puzzles, designer gift wrap, stationery sets, and bookmarks. For more information or to place an order, please contact Pomegranate Communications, Inc.: 800-227-1428; www.pomegranate.com.

COVER IMAGE: Cherry blossom viewing (detail), approx. 1615–1700
Japan, Edo period (1615–1868)
Two panels from a six-panel screen, ink, colors, and gold on paper, 60 x 144 in. (image)
The Avery Brundage Collection, B62D9+

Designed by Lisa Reid

Dates in color indicate federal holidays.
All astronomical data supplied in this calendar are expressed in Greenwich Mean Time (GMT).
Moon phases and American, Canadian, and UK holidays are noted.

● NEW MOON   ☽ FIRST QUARTER   ○ FULL MOON   ☾ LAST QUARTER

The answer to the question "What is Asian art?" is as multifaceted as the many cultures that have created this art. A Durga mandala from Nepal, for instance, is an aid to meditation, while a headcloth from the southern Philippines signifies the social standing of the wearer. A Korean scroll painting of a mayor's inaugural procession documents a historic secular event, while an Indian miniature depicting the deities Vishnu and Lakshmi riding a mythical bird symbolizes sacred values.

But of which religion? Home to 60 percent of the world's peoples, Asia is also the place of origin of many of the world's great faiths, among them Buddhism, Confucianism, Hinduism, Islam, Sikhism, and Taoism, as well as of belief systems practiced by smaller groups of people. Even religions associated primarily with cultures outside Asia, such as Christianity, have found expression in Asian art.

Searching, then, for a single unifying thread among the continent's many traditions is an impossible task. Instead we can focus on some of Asia's individual traditions, and from these we can gain a sense of the whole.

In this calendar's stunning assemblage of works on cloth and paper from the Asian Art Museum of San Francisco, home to one of the largest collections of Asian art in the Western world, several cultures come into focus. Cotton and silk textiles, paintings on paper, and works of calligraphy suggest the richness of South, West, and Southeast Asia. Tibetan Buddhist devotional paintings *(thangkas)* give a sense of the bold, vibrant art of the Himalayas. A particularly rich selection of works from China includes religious works, landscapes, and still lifes. Religious paintings from Thailand express that culture's interpretation of Buddhism. And a brilliant group of Japanese paintings hints at the range and depth of a long and distinguished tradition.

While the arts of Asia cannot be encapsulated in thirty-two images, each of these works is a masterpiece that reflects the refined vision of an accomplished Asian artist at a moment of particular inspiration. Perhaps vision, mastery, and inspiration are, after all, what constitute the unifying thread of Asian art.

2007

JANUARY

s	m	t	w	t	f	s
	1	2	3	4	5	6
7	8	9	10	11	12	13
14	15	16	17	18	19	20
21	22	23	24	25	26	27
28	29	30	31			

FEBRUARY

s	m	t	w	t	f	s
				1	2	3
4	5	6	7	8	9	10
11	12	13	14	15	16	17
18	19	20	21	22	23	24
25	26	27	28			

MARCH

s	m	t	w	t	f	s
				1	2	3
4	5	6	7	8	9	10
11	12	13	14	15	16	17
18	19	20	21	22	23	24
25	26	27	28	29	30	31

APRIL

s	m	t	w	t	f	s
1	2	3	4	5	6	7
8	9	10	11	12	13	14
15	16	17	18	19	20	21
22	23	24	25	26	27	28
29	30					

MAY

s	m	t	w	t	f	s
		1	2	3	4	5
6	7	8	9	10	11	12
13	14	15	16	17	18	19
20	21	22	23	24	25	26
27	28	29	30	31		

JUNE

s	m	t	w	t	f	s
					1	2
3	4	5	6	7	8	9
10	11	12	13	14	15	16
17	18	19	20	21	22	23
24	25	26	27	28	29	30

2007

JULY

s	m	t	w	t	f	s
1	2	3	4	5	6	7
8	9	10	11	12	13	14
15	16	17	18	19	20	21
22	23	24	25	26	27	28
29	30	31				

AUGUST

s	m	t	w	t	f	s
			1	2	3	4
5	6	7	8	9	10	11
12	13	14	15	16	17	18
19	20	21	22	23	24	25
26	27	28	29	30	31	

SEPTEMBER

s	m	t	w	t	f	s
						1
2	3	4	5	6	7	8
9	10	11	12	13	14	15
16	17	18	19	20	21	22
23/30	24	25	26	27	28	29

OCTOBER

s	m	t	w	t	f	s
	1	2	3	4	5	6
7	8	9	10	11	12	13
14	15	16	17	18	19	20
21	22	23	24	25	26	27
28	29	30	31			

NOVEMBER

s	m	t	w	t	f	s
				1	2	3
4	5	6	7	8	9	10
11	12	13	14	15	16	17
18	19	20	21	22	23	24
25	26	27	28	29	30	

DECEMBER

s	m	t	w	t	f	s
						1
2	3	4	5	6	7	8
9	10	11	12	13	14	15
16	17	18	19	20	21	22
23/30	24/31	25	26	27	28	29

Flowering plants, approx. 1800–1900
Watanabe Shiko (1683–1755)
Japan
Hanging scroll, ink and colors on silk, 38⅞ x 14⅛ in.
The Avery Brundage Collection, B72D40

JANUARY

SUNDAY	MONDAY	TUESDAY	WEDNESDAY	THURSDAY	FRIDAY	SATURDAY
	1	2	3 ○	4	5	6
7	8	9	10	11 ☽	12	13
14	15	16	17	18	19 ●	20
21	22	23	24	25 ☽	26	27
28	29	30	31			

JAN 1   NEW YEAR'S DAY
JAN 2   BANK HOLIDAY (SCOTLAND)
JAN 15   MARTIN LUTHER KING JR. DAY

JANUARY

monday _____

1 **1**

tuesday _____

2 **2**

wednesday _____

3 **3** ○

thursday _____

4 **4**

friday _____

5 **5**

saturday _____

6 **6**

sunday _____

7 **7**

JANUARY

monday
8
8

tuesday
9
9

wednesday
10
10

thursday
☾ 11
11

friday
12
12

saturday
13
13

s	m	t	w	t	f	s
	1	2	3	4	5	6
7	8	9	10	11	12	13
14	15	16	17	18	19	20
21	22	23	24	25	26	27
28	29	30	31			

JANUARY

sunday
14
14

Maitreya, the Buddha of the Future, 1800–1900
Tibet
Colors and gold on cotton, 94 x 53 in. (overall)
The Avery Brundage Collection, B60D54

JANUARY

monday

MARTIN LUTHER KING JR. DAY

15 15

tuesday

16 16

wednesday

17 17

thursday

18 18

friday

● **19** 19

saturday

20 20

s	m	t	w	t	f	s
	1	2	3	4	5	6
7	8	9	10	11	12	13
14	15	16	17	18	19	20
21	22	23	24	25	26	27
28	29	30	31			

JANUARY

sunday

21 21

Landscape
Fang Yizhi (1611–1671)
China, Ming dynasty (1368–1644)
Hanging scroll, ink and colors on paper,
57 1/2 x 17 3/4 in. (image)
Museum purchase, B74D3

JANUARY

monday

22 22

tuesday

23 23

wednesday

24 24

thursday

☽ **25** 25

friday

26 26

saturday

27 27

s	m	t	w	t	f	s
	1	2	3	4	5	6
7	8	9	10	11	12	13
14	15	16	17	18	19	20
21	22	23	24	25	26	27
28	29	30	31			

JANUARY

sunday

28 28

JAN/FEB

29 **29**

30 **30**

31 **31**

32 **1**

33 **2** ◯

34 **3**

35 **4**

FEBRUARY

SUNDAY	MONDAY	TUESDAY	WEDNESDAY	THURSDAY	FRIDAY	SATURDAY
				1	2 ○	3
4	5	6	7	8	9	10 ☽
11	12	13	14	15	16	17 ●
18	19	20	21	22	23	24 ☾
25	26	27	28			

FEB 12   LINCOLN'S BIRTHDAY   FEB 21   ASH WEDNESDAY

FEB 14   VALENTINE'S DAY   FEB 22   WASHINGTON'S BIRTHDAY

FEB 19   PRESIDENTS' DAY

其是神通力 十方諸國土
廣修智方便 無剎不現身

The Bodhisattva Avalokiteshvara (Gwaneum Bosal)
approx. 1600–1800
Korea, Joseon dynasty (1392–1910)
Hanging scroll, ink and colors on linen, 69½ x 29 in.
The Avery Brundage Collection, B65D44

FEBRUARY

s	m	t	w	t	f	s
				1	2	3
4	5	6	7	8	9	10
11	12	13	14	15	16	17
18	19	20	21	22	23	24
25	26	27	28			

FEBRUARY

Scene from a manuscript of the Ramayana (Life of Rama), approx. 1800–1825
Central Thailand
Pigments and gold on paper, 8¾ x 19½ in.
Gift from Doris Duke Charitable Foundation's Southeast Asian Art Collection, F2002.27.9

FEBRUARY

LINCOLN'S BIRTHDAY

VALENTINE'S DAY

s	m	t	w	t	f	s
				1	2	3
4	5	6	7	8	9	10
11	12	13	14	15	16	17
18	19	20	21	22	23	24
25	26	27	28			

FEBRUARY

Sunbirds, approx. 1850
India
Watercolor on paper, 7¼ x 11½ in.
Gift of Mr. and Mrs. Willard G. Clark, 1988.2

FEBRUARY

PRESIDENTS' DAY

19 50

20 51

ASH WEDNESDAY

21 52

WASHINGTON'S BIRTHDAY

22 53

23 54

☽ **24** 55

s	m	t	w	t	f	s
				1	2	3
4	5	6	7	8	9	10
11	12	13	14	15	16	17
18	19	20	21	22	23	24
25	26	27	28			

FEBRUARY

25 56

FEB/MAR

monday
57 **26**

tuesday
58 **27**

wednesday
59 **28**

thursday
60 **1**

friday
61 **2**

saturday
62 **3** ○   PURIM (BEGINS AT SUNSET)

sunday
63 **4**

MARCH

SUNDAY	MONDAY	TUESDAY	WEDNESDAY	THURSDAY	FRIDAY	SATURDAY
				1	2	3 ○
4	5	6	7	8	9	10
11	12 ☾	13	14	15	16	17
18	19 ●	20	21	22	23	24
25 ☽	26	27	28	29	30	31

MAR 3   PURIM (BEGINS AT SUNSET)

MAR 8   INTERNATIONAL WOMEN'S DAY

MAR 11   DAYLIGHT SAVING TIME BEGINS

MAR 17   ST. PATRICK'S DAY

MAR 18   MOTHERING SUNDAY (UK)

MAR 21   VERNAL EQUINOX 12:07 AM (GMT)

MAR 25   SUMMER TIME BEGINS (UK)

The Wheel of Life, 1800–1900
Tibet
Colors on cotton, 26¼ x 18½ in. (image)
Gift of Walter and Josephine Landor, 2001.49

monday

5 64

tuesday

6 65

wednesday

7 66

INTERNATIONAL WOMEN'S DAY

thursday

8 67

friday

9 68

saturday

10 69

s	m	t	w	t	f	s
				1	2	3
4	5	6	7	8	9	10
11	12	13	14	15	16	17
18	19	20	21	22	23	24
25	26	27	28	29	30	31

MARCH

DAYLIGHT SAVING TIME BEGINS

sunday

11 70

MARCH

monday

71 **12** ☾

tuesday

72 **13**

wednesday

73 **14**

thursday

74 **15**

friday

75 **16**

saturday

76 **17**   ST. PATRICK'S DAY

sunday

77 **18**   MOTHERING SUNDAY (UK)

MARCH

tuesday
20 79

VERNAL EQUINOX 12:07 AM (GMT)

wednesday
21 80

thursday
22 81

friday
23 82

saturday
24 83

s	m	t	w	t	f	s
				1	2	3
4	5	6	7	8	9	10
11	12	13	14	15	16	17
18	19	20	21	22	23	24
25	26	27	28	29	30	31

MARCH

SUMMER TIME BEGINS (UK)

sunday
25 84

River scene after Wang Wei's painting of Wangchuan (detail), 1574
Song Xu
China, Ming dynasty, reign of the Wanli emperor (1573–1619)
Handscroll, ink and colors on silk, 12 3/8 x 350 in. (image)
Museum purchase, B67D2

monday

26 85

tuesday

27 86

wednesday

28 87

thursday

29 88

friday

30 89

saturday

31 90

s	m	t	w	t	f	s
	1	2	3	4	5	6	7
8	9	10	11	12	13	14
15	16	17	18	19	20	21
22	23	24	25	26	27	28
29	30					

APRIL

PALM SUNDAY

sunday

1 91

Calligraphy page inscribed with poetic verses, approx. 1501–1545
Mir'Ali Haravi (died 1544 or 1545)
Iran, Safavid dynasty (1501–1732)
Ink and colors on paper, 8½ x 5⅛ in.
Gift of the Todd G. Williams Memorial Fund and the Society for Asian Art, B87D6

APRIL

SUNDAY	MONDAY	TUESDAY	WEDNESDAY	THURSDAY	FRIDAY	SATURDAY
1	2 ○	3	4	5	6	7
8	9	10 ☾	11	12	13	14
15	16	17 ●	18	19	20	21
22	23	24 ☽	25	26	27	28
29	30					

APR 1	PALM SUNDAY		APR 8	EASTER SUNDAY
APR 2	PASSOVER (BEGINS AT SUNSET)		APR 9	EASTER MONDAY (CANADA, UK)
APR 6	GOOD FRIDAY		APR 22	EARTH DAY

APRIL

monday

92 **2** ◯   PASSOVER (BEGINS AT SUNSET)

tuesday

93 **3**

wednesday

94 **4**

thursday

95 **5**

friday

96 **6**   GOOD FRIDAY

saturday

97 **7**

sunday

98 **8**   EASTER SUNDAY

monday

9 99

EASTER MONDAY (CANADA, UK)

tuesday

☽ **10** 100

wednesday

11 101

thursday

12 102

friday

13 103

saturday

14 104

s	m	t	w	t	f	s
1	2	3	4	5	6	7
8	9	10	11	12	13	14
15	16	17	18	19	20	21
22	23	24	25	26	27	28
29	30					

sunday

15 105

APRIL

Lily and pinks, from *Flowers of the Twelve Months*
Yun Bing (active 1670–1710)
China, Qing dynasty, reign of the Kangxi emperor (1662–1722)
Album leaf, ink and colors on silk, 16¹⁄₈ x 13 in.
The Avery Brundage Collection, B65D49.e

monday
16 106

tuesday
● 17 107

wednesday
18 108

thursday
19 109

friday
20 110

saturday
21 111

s	m	t	w	t	f	s
1	2	3	4	5	6	7
8	9	10	11	12	13	14
15	16	17	18	19	20	21
22	23	24	25	26	27	28
29	30					

APRIL

EARTH DAY

sunday
22 112

Mandala of the Hindu deity Durga, approx. 1500
Nepal
Colors on cotton, 31 x 25¼ in.
Gift of Margaret Polak, B87D22

APRIL

monday
23 113

tuesday
☽ 24 114

wednesday
25 115

thursday
26 116

friday
27 117

saturday
28 118

s	m	t	w	t	f	s
1	2	3	4	5	6	7
8	9	10	11	12	13	14
15	16	17	18	19	20	21
22	23	24	25	26	27	28
29	30					

APRIL

sunday
29 119

APR/MAY

monday

120 **30**

tuesday

121 **1**

wednesday

122 **2** ◯

thursday

123 **3**

friday

124 **4**

saturday

125 **5**

CINCO DE MAYO

sunday

126 **6**

MAY

SUNDAY	MONDAY	TUESDAY	WEDNESDAY	THURSDAY	FRIDAY	SATURDAY
		1	2 ○	3	4	5
6	7	8	9	10 ☾	11	12
13	14	15	16 ●	17	18	19
20	21	22	23 ☽	24	25	26
27	28	29	30	31		

MAY 5	CINCO DE MAYO	MAY 21	VICTORIA DAY (CANADA)
MAY 7	BANK HOLIDAY (UK)	MAY 28	MEMORIAL DAY OBSERVED
MAY 13	MOTHER'S DAY		BANK HOLIDAY (UK)
MAY 19	ARMED FORCES DAY	MAY 30	MEMORIAL DAY

Quail and millet, 1720–1772
Tosa Mitsuyoshi (1700–1772)
Japan, Edo period (1615–1868)
Hanging scroll, ink and colors on silk, 15 x 23³/₈ in. (image)
Gift of Jeanne G. O'Brien in memory of James E. O'Brien, 1993.33

BANK HOLIDAY (UK)

monday
7 127

tuesday
8 128

wednesday
9 129

thursday
☾ **10** 130

friday
11 131

saturday
12 132

s	m	t	w	t	f	s
		1	2	3	4	5
6	7	8	9	10	11	12
13	14	15	16	17	18	19
20	21	22	23	24	25	26
27	28	29	30	31		

MAY

MOTHER'S DAY

sunday
13 133

MAY

monday
134 **14**

tuesday
135 **15**

wednesday
136 **16** ●

thursday
137 **17**

friday
138 **18**

saturday
139 **19**   ARMED FORCES DAY

sunday
140 **20**

monday

21 141

VICTORIA DAY (CANADA)

tuesday

22 142

wednesday

☽ **23** 143

thursday

24 144

friday

25 145

saturday

26 146

s	m	t	w	t	f	s
		1	2	3	4	5
6	7	8	9	10	11	12
13	14	15	16	17	18	19
20	21	22	23	24	25	26
27	28	29	30	31		

MAY

sunday

27 147

Abbot Hyegak's *dancheong* patterns (detail), 1990–1995
Dongweon and others
The Republic of Korea (1948–)
Panel from a folding screen, ink, mineral colors,
and gold on paper, 101 x 22 in. (each panel)
Gift of Abbot Hyegak and Dongweon, 1995.35

MAY/JUN

MEMORIAL DAY OBSERVED

BANK HOLIDAY (UK)

monday

28 148

tuesday

29 149

MEMORIAL DAY

wednesday

30 150

thursday

31 151

friday

○ **1** 152

saturday

2 153

s	m	t	w	t	f	s
					1	2
3	4	5	6	7	8	9
10	11	12	13	14	15	16
17	18	19	20	21	22	23
24	25	26	27	28	29	30

JUNE

sunday

3 154

Blossoming trees (detail), approx. 1700–1800
Japan, Edo period (1615–1868)
From a pair of six-panel screens, ink, color, and gold on paper, 61⅜ x 142 in.
The Avery Brundage Collection, B60D10

JUNE

SUNDAY	MONDAY	TUESDAY	WEDNESDAY	THURSDAY	FRIDAY	SATURDAY
					1 ○	2
3	4	5	6	7	8 ☾	9
10	11	12	13	14	15 ●	16
17	18	19	20	21	22 ☽	23
24	25	26	27	28	29	30 ○

JUN 14   FLAG DAY
JUN 17   FATHER'S DAY
JUN 21   SUMMER SOLSTICE 6:06 PM (GMT)

JUNE

monday
155 4

tuesday
156 5

wednesday
157 6

thursday
158 7

friday
159 8 ☾

saturday
160 9

sunday
161 10

monday

11

tuesday

12

wednesday

13

thursday

FLAG DAY

14

friday

● **15**

saturday

16

s	m	t	w	t	f	s
					1	2
3	4	5	6	7	8	9
10	11	12	13	14	15	16
17	18	19	20	21	22	23
24	25	26	27	28	29	30

JUNE

sunday

FATHER'S DAY

17

Gathering of immortals at Yaochi, 1700–1800
China, Qing dynasty (1644–1911)
Hanging scroll, painted slit silk (*kesi*) tapestry, 72$\frac{1}{4}$ x 41$\frac{1}{4}$ in.
The Avery Brundage Collection, B62D28

monday
18 ₁₆₉

tuesday
19 ₁₇₀

wednesday
20 ₁₇₁

SUMMER SOLSTICE 6:06 PM (GMT)

thursday
21 ₁₇₂

friday
☽ **22** ₁₇₃

saturday
23 ₁₇₄

s	m	t	w	t	f	s
					1	2
3	4	5	6	7	8	9
10	11	12	13	14	15	16
17	18	19	20	21	22	23
24	25	26	27	28	29	30

JUNE

sunday
24 ₁₇₅

Scene from a manuscript of the Ramayana (Life of Rama), approx. 1800–1825
Central Thailand
Pigments and gold on paper, 8³⁄₄ x 19¹⁄₂ in.
Gift from Doris Duke Charitable Foundation's Southeast Asian Art Collection, F2002.27.9

monday
25 176

tuesday
26 177

wednesday
27 178

thursday
28 179

friday
29 180

saturday
○ **30** 181

s	m	t	w	t	f	s
	1	2	3	4	5	6	7
8	9	10	11	12	13	14
15	16	17	18	19	20	21
22	23	24	25	26	27	28
29	30	31				

JULY

CANADA DAY (CANADA)

sunday
1 182

Headcloth, 1900–1960
Southern Philippines, Tausug people, Sulu archipelago
Tapestry weave silk, 32$\frac{1}{8}$ x 33$\frac{1}{2}$ in.
The Avery Brundage Collection, 1993.25

JULY

SUNDAY	MONDAY	TUESDAY	WEDNESDAY	THURSDAY	FRIDAY	SATURDAY
1	2	3	4	5	6	7 ☽
8	9	10	11	12	13	14 ●
15	16	17	18	19	20	21
22 ☽	23	24	25	26	27	28
29	30 ○	31				

JUL 1   CANADA DAY (CANADA)   JUL 4   INDEPENDENCE DAY
JUL 2   CANADA DAY OBSERVED (CANADA)   JUL 12   BANK HOLIDAY (N. IRELAND)

JULY

monday
183   2
CANADA DAY OBSERVED (CANADA)

tuesday
184   3

wednesday
185   4
INDEPENDENCE DAY

thursday
186   5

friday
187   6

saturday
188   7 ☾

sunday
189   8

JULY

monday
9 190

tuesday
10 191

wednesday
11 192

thursday
BANK HOLIDAY (N. IRELAND)
12 193

friday
13 194

saturday
● 14 195

s	m	t	w	t	f	s
1	2	3	4	5	6	7
8	9	10	11	12	13	14
15	16	17	18	19	20	21
22	23	24	25	26	27	28
29	30	31				

JULY

sunday
15 196

The Cosmic Buddha Amoghasiddhi, approx. 1275–1350
Tibet, Sakya Monastery
Colors on cloth, 33¹⁄₂ x 26¹⁄₄ in. (image)
Museum purchase, City Arts Trust Fund, 1991.3

JULY

monday
16 <small>197</small>

tuesday
17 <small>198</small>

wednesday
18 <small>199</small>

thursday
19 <small>200</small>

friday
20 <small>201</small>

saturday
21 <small>202</small>

s	m	t	w	t	f	s
1	2	3	4	5	6	7
8	9	10	11	12	13	14
15	16	17	18	19	20	21
22	23	24	25	26	27	28
29	30	31				

JULY

sunday
☽ 22 <small>203</small>

Maple tree and moon, 1600–1700
Japan, Edo period (1615–1868)
Two-panel screen, ink and colors on gold paper, 59 ¼ x 67 ½ in. (image)
The Avery Brundage Collection, 1999.9

JULY

monday

23 204

tuesday

24 205

wednesday

25 206

thursday

26 207

friday

27 208

saturday

28 209

s	m	t	w	t	f	s
1	2	3	4	5	6	7
8	9	10	11	12	13	14
15	16	17	18	19	20	21
22	23	24	25	26	27	28
29	30	31				

JULY

sunday

29 210

JUL/AUG

monday ———
211 **30** ○

tuesday ———
212 **31**

wednesday ———————————————————————————————————————
213 **1**

thursday ——
214 **2**

friday ——
215 **3**

saturday ——
216 **4**

sunday ——
217 **5** ☾

AUGUST

SUNDAY	MONDAY	TUESDAY	WEDNESDAY	THURSDAY	FRIDAY	SATURDAY
			1	2	3	4
5 ☽	6	7	8	9	10	11
12 ●	13	14	15	16	17	18
19	20 ☽	21	22	23	24	25
26	27	28 ○	29	30	31	

AUG 6   CIVIC HOLIDAY (CANADA, MOST PROVINCES)
          BANK HOLIDAY (SCOTLAND)
AUG 27 BANK HOLIDAY (UK EXCEPT SCOTLAND)

AUGUST

monday
218 **6**

CIVIC HOLIDAY (CANADA, MOST PROVINCES)
BANK HOLIDAY (SCOTLAND)

tuesday
219 **7**

wednesday
220 **8**

thursday
221 **9**

friday
222 **10**

saturday
223 **11**

sunday
224 **12** ●

AUGUST

13 225

14 226

15 227

16 228

17 229

18 230

s	m	t	w	t	f	s
			1	2	3	4
5	6	7	8	9	10	11
12	13	14	15	16	17	18
19	20	21	22	23	24	25
26	27	28	29	30	31	

AUGUST

19 231

Inaugural procession to Anneung (detail), dated 1786
Attributed to Gim Hong-do (1745–before 1818)
Korea, Joseon dynasty (1392–1910)
Handscroll, ink and colors on paper, 12¹/₂ x 252 in.
Gift of Evelyn B. McCune in memory of George McAfee McCune, 1991.181

AUGUST

☽ **20** 232

21 233

22 234

23 235

24 236

25 237

26 238

s	m	t	w	t	f	s
			1	2	3	4
5	6	7	8	9	10	11
12	13	14	15	16	17	18
19	20	21	22	23	24	25
26	27	28	29	30	31	

AUGUST

The Hindu deity Vishnu and his consort Lakshmi on the man-bird Garuda, approx. 1760
India, former kingdom of Bundi, Rajasthan state
Colors on paper, 8⅝ x 6 in.
Gift of George Hopper Fitch, B84D3

monday

BANK HOLIDAY (UK EXCEPT SCOTLAND)

27 239

tuesday

○ 28 240

wednesday

29 241

thursday

30 242

friday

31 243

saturday

1 244

s	m	t	w	t	f	s
						1
2	3	4	5	6	7	8
9	10	11	12	13	14	15
16	17	18	19	20	21	22
23	24	25	26	27	28	29
30						

SEPTEMBER

sunday

2 245

Abbot Hyegak's *dancheong* patterns (detail), 1990–1995
Dongweon and others
The Republic of Korea (1948–)
Panel from a folding screen, ink, mineral colors,
and gold on paper, 101 x 22 in. (each panel)
Gift of Abbot Hyegak and Dongweon, 1995.35

SEPTEMBER

SUNDAY	MONDAY	TUESDAY	WEDNESDAY	THURSDAY	FRIDAY	SATURDAY
						1
2	3	4 ☽	5	6	7	8
9	10	11 ●	12	13	14	15
16	17	18	19 ☽	20	21	22
23	24	25	26 ○	27	28	29
30						

SEP 3   LABOR DAY (US, CANADA)

SEP 12   ROSH HASHANAH (BEGINS AT SUNSET)

SEP 21   YOM KIPPUR (BEGINS AT SUNSET)

SEP 23   AUTUMNAL EQUINOX 9:51 AM (GMT)

SEPTEMBER

monday _____
LABOR DAY (US, CANADA)
246 3

tuesday _____
247 4 ☾

wednesday _____
248 5

thursday _____
249 6

friday _____
250 7

saturday _____
251 8

sunday _____
252 9

SEPTEMBER

monday
10 253

tuesday
● 11 254

wednesday
12 255

ROSH HASHANAH (BEGINS AT SUNSET)

thursday
13 256

friday
14 257

saturday
15 258

s	m	t	w	t	f	s
						1
2	3	4	5	6	7	8
9	10	11	12	13	14	15
16	17	18	19	20	21	22
23	24	25	26	27	28	29
30						

SEPTEMBER

sunday
16 259

Scene from a manuscript of the Ramayana (Life of Rama), approx. 1800–1825
Central Thailand
Pigments and gold on paper, 8³⁄₄ x 19¹⁄₂ in.
Gift from Doris Duke Charitable Foundation's Southeast Asian Art Collection, F2002.27.9

SEPTEMBER

YOM KIPPUR (BEGINS AT SUNSET)

s	m	t	w	t	f	s
						1
2	3	4	5	6	7	8
9	10	11	12	13	14	15
16	17	18	19	20	21	22
23	24	25	26	27	28	29
30						

SEPTEMBER

AUTUMNAL EQUINOX 9:51 AM (GMT)

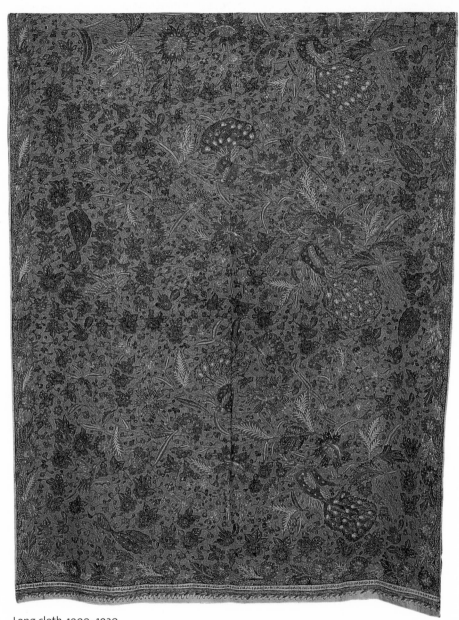

Long cloth, 1900–1930
Tjoa Tjoen Tiang
Indonesia, Solo, Central Java
Cotton batik, 42 x 103 in.
Gift of Emily Sano in honor of Rosina and Tony Sun, 2002.27

SEPTEMBER

monday
24 ₂₆₇

tuesday
25 ₂₆₈

wednesday
○ ## 26 ₂₆₉

thursday
27 ₂₇₀

friday
28 ₂₇₁

saturday
29 ₂₇₂

s	m	t	w	t	f	s
						1
2	3	4	5	6	7	8
9	10	11	12	13	14	15
16	17	18	19	20	21	22
23	24	25	26	27	28	29
30						

SEPTEMBER

sunday
30 ₂₇₃

A scene from the novel *Nine Cloud Dream* (detail), 1800–1900
Signed Yijae
Korea, Joseon dynasty (1392–1910)
Panel from an eight-panel screen, ink and colors on paper, 64 x 168 in. (overall)
Acquisition made possible in part by the Korean Art and Culture Committee, 1997.21

OCTOBER

SUNDAY	MONDAY	TUESDAY	WEDNESDAY	THURSDAY	FRIDAY	SATURDAY
	1	2	3 ☽	4	5	6
7	8	9	10	11 ●	12	13
14	15	16	17	18	19 ☽	20
21	22	23	24	25	26 ○	27
28	29	30	31			

OCT 8	COLUMBUS DAY OBSERVED	OCT 24	UNITED NATIONS DAY
	THANKSGIVING DAY (CANADA)	OCT 28	SUMMER TIME ENDS (UK)
OCT 12	COLUMBUS DAY	OCT 31	HALLOWEEN

OCTOBER

274 **1**

275 **2**

276 **3** ☾

277 **4**

278 **5**

279 **6**

280 **7**

OCTOBER

8

COLUMBUS DAY OBSERVED

THANKSGIVING DAY (CANADA)

9

10

11

12

COLUMBUS DAY

13

14

s	m	t	w	t	f	s
	1	2	3	4	5	6
7	8	9	10	11	12	13
14	15	16	17	18	19	20
21	22	23	24	25	26	27
28	29	30	31			

OCTOBER

Jacket, 1920–1970
Indonesia, Gayo people, Aceh, Sumatra
Embroidered cotton with shell appliqué, 27⅝ x 51⅝ in.
Museum purchase, 2002.28

OCTOBER

monday
15 288

tuesday
16 289

wednesday
17 290

thursday
18 291

friday
☽ **19** 292

saturday
20 293

s	m	t	w	t	f	s
	1	2	3	4	5	6
7	8	9	10	11	12	13
14	15	16	17	18	19	20
21	22	23	24	25	26	27
28	29	30	31			

OCTOBER

sunday
21 294

The Refuge Tree of the Gelug Order, 1700–1800
Tibet
Colors on cotton, 42 x 28 in. (image)
Gift of the Xianming Ge Collection, 2000.29

OCTOBER

UNITED NATIONS DAY

s	m	t	w	t	f	s
	1	2	3	4	5	6
7	8	9	10	11	12	13
14	15	16	17	18	19	20
21	22	23	24	25	26	27
28	29	30	31			

OCTOBER

SUMMER TIME ENDS (UK)

OCT/NOV

monday

302 **29**

tuesday

303 **30**

wednesday   HALLOWEEN

304 **31**

thursday

305 **1** ☾

friday

306 **2**

saturday

307 **3**

sunday   DAYLIGHT SAVING TIME ENDS

308 **4**

NOVEMBER

SUNDAY	MONDAY	TUESDAY	WEDNESDAY	THURSDAY	FRIDAY	SATURDAY
				1 ☾	2	3
4	5	6	7	8	9 ●	10
11	12	13	14	15	16	17 ☽
18	19	20	21	22	23	24 ○
25	26	27	28	29	30	

NOV 4   DAYLIGHT SAVING TIME ENDS   NOV 12   VETERANS DAY OBSERVED

NOV 11   VETERANS DAY   NOV 22   THANKSGIVING DAY

        REMEMBRANCE DAY (CANADA)

NOVEMBER

monday

309   5

tuesday

310   6

wednesday

311   7

thursday

312   8

friday

313   9 ⬤

saturday

314   10

sunday

315   11

VETERANS DAY

REMEMBRANCE DAY (CANADA)

monday

12 316

VETERANS DAY OBSERVED

tuesday

13 317

wednesday

14 318

thursday

15 319

friday

16 320

saturday

☽ **17** 321

sunday

18 322

s	m	t	w	t	f	s
				1	2	3
4	5	6	7	8	9	10
11	12	13	14	15	16	17
18	19	20	21	22	23	24
25	26	27	28	29	30	

NOVEMBER

Guru Nanak meeting with his brother-in-law, Jai Ram, approx. 1755–1770
India, probably Murshidabad, West Bengal state
Colors on paper
Gift of the Kapany Collection, 1998.58.5

NOVEMBER

monday

19 ₃₂₃

tuesday

20 ₃₂₄

wednesday

21 ₃₂₅

thursday

THANKSGIVING DAY

22 ₃₂₆

friday

23 ₃₂₇

saturday

○ **24** ₃₂₈

s	m	t	w	t	f	s
				1	2	3
4	5	6	7	8	9	10
11	12	13	14	15	16	17
18	19	20	21	22	23	24
25	26	27	28	29	30	

NOVEMBER

sunday

25 ₃₂₉

Tribute Bearers (detail), approx. 1350
Ren Bowen
China, Yuan dynasty (1280–1368)
Handscroll, ink, colors, and gold on silk, 13⅝ x 86¹³/₁₆ in.
The Avery Brundage Collection, B60D100

monday

26 ₃₃₀

tuesday

27 ₃₃₁

wednesday

28 ₃₃₂

thursday

29 ₃₃₃

friday

30 ₃₃₄

saturday

☽ **1** ₃₃₅

s	m	t	w	t	f	s
						1
2	3	4	5	6	7	8
9	10	11	12	13	14	15
16	17	18	19	20	21	22
23	24	25	26	27	28	29
30	31					

DECEMBER

sunday

2 ₃₃₆

The Persian hero Rustam slaying a dragon, from a manuscript of the Shahnama (Book of Kings), 1600–1650
Northern India or Pakistan
Colors on paper, 10¹⁄₄ x 6 in.
Gift of George Hopper Fitch, B74D20

DECEMBER

SUNDAY	MONDAY	TUESDAY	WEDNESDAY	THURSDAY	FRIDAY	SATURDAY
						1 ☾
2	3	4	5	6	7	8
9 ●	10	11	12	13	14	15
16	17 ☽	18	19	20	21	22
23	24 ○	25	26	27	28	29
30	31 ☾					

DEC 4   HANUKKAH (BEGINS AT SUNSET)
DEC 22   WINTER SOLSTICE 6:08 AM (GMT)
DEC 25   CHRISTMAS DAY
DEC 26   BOXING DAY (CANADA, UK)
          KWANZAA BEGINS

DECEMBER

monday

337   3

tuesday

HANUKKAH (BEGINS AT SUNSET)

338   4

wednesday

339   5

thursday

340   6

friday

341   7

saturday

342   8

sunday

343   9 ●

DECEMBER

10 344

11 345

12 346

13 347

14 348

15 349

s	m	t	w	t	f	s
						1
2	3	4	5	6	7	8
9	10	11	12	13	14	15
16	17	18	19	20	21	22
23	24	25	26	27	28	29
30	31					

DECEMBER

16 350

Cherry blossom viewing (detail), approx. 1615–1700
Japan, Edo period (1615–1868)
Two panels from a six-panel screen, ink, colors, and gold on paper, 60 x 144 in. (image)
The Avery Brundage Collection, B62D9+

DECEMBER

☽ **17** 351

tuesday
18 352

wednesday
19 353

thursday
20 354

friday
21 355

WINTER SOLSTICE 6:08 AM (GMT)

saturday
22 356

s	m	t	w	t	f	s
						1
2	3	4	5	6	7	8
9	10	11	12	13	14	15
16	17	18	19	20	21	22
23	24	25	26	27	28	29
30	31					

DECEMBER

sunday
23 357

Rabbit and moon
Watanabe Shotei (1851–1918)
Japan
Hanging scroll, ink and colors on silk,
34 1/8 x 10 3/4 in. (image)
Gift of Jeanne G. O'Brien in memory of
James E. O'Brien, 1993.44

DECEMBER

○ **24** 358

CHRISTMAS DAY

25 359

BOXING DAY (CANADA, UK)

KWANZAA BEGINS

26 360

27 361

28 362

29 363

30 364

s	m	t	w	t	f	s
						1
2	3	4	5	6	7	8
9	10	11	12	13	14	15
16	17	18	19	20	21	22
23	24	25	26	27	28	29
30	31					

DECEMBER

DEC/JAN

monday

365 **31** ☾

tuesday

NEW YEAR'S DAY

1 **1**

wednesday

BANK HOLIDAY (SCOTLAND)

2 **2**

thursday

3 **3**

friday

4 **4**

saturday

5 **5**

sunday

6 **6**

JANUARY

7 7

tuesday
● 8 8

wednesday
9 9

thursday
10 10

friday
11 11

saturday
12 12

s	m	t	w	t	f	s
		1	2	3	4	5
6	7	8	9	10	11	12
13	14	15	16	17	18	19
20	21	22	23	24	25	26
27	28	29	30	31		

JANUARY

sunday
13 13

2008

JANUARY

s	m	t	w	t	f	s
		1	2	3	4	5
6	7	8	9	10	11	12
13	14	15	16	17	18	19
20	21	22	23	24	25	26
27	28	29	30	31		

FEBRUARY

s	m	t	w	t	f	s
					1	2
3	4	5	6	7	8	9
10	11	12	13	14	15	16
17	18	19	20	21	22	23
24	25	26	27	28	29	

MARCH

s	m	t	w	t	f	s
						1
2	3	4	5	6	7	8
9	10	11	12	13	14	15
16	17	18	19	20	21	22
23/30	24/31	25	26	27	28	29

APRIL

s	m	t	w	t	f	s
		1	2	3	4	5
6	7	8	9	10	11	12
13	14	15	16	17	18	19
20	21	22	23	24	25	26
27	28	29	30			

MAY

s	m	t	w	t	f	s
				1	2	3
4	5	6	7	8	9	10
11	12	13	14	15	16	17
18	19	20	21	22	23	24
25	26	27	28	29	30	31

JUNE

s	m	t	w	t	f	s
1	2	3	4	5	6	7
8	9	10	11	12	13	14
15	16	17	18	19	20	21
22	23	24	25	26	27	28
29	30					

2008

JULY

s	m	t	w	t	f	s
		1	2	3	4	5
6	7	8	9	10	11	12
13	14	15	16	17	18	19
20	21	22	23	24	25	26
27	28	29	30	31		

AUGUST

s	m	t	w	t	f	s
					1	2
3	4	5	6	7	8	9
10	11	12	13	14	15	16
17	18	19	20	21	22	23
24/31	25	26	27	28	29	30

SEPTEMBER

s	m	t	w	t	f	s
	1	2	3	4	5	6
7	8	9	10	11	12	13
14	15	16	17	18	19	20
21	22	23	24	25	26	27
28	29	30				

OCTOBER

s	m	t	w	t	f	s
			1	2	3	4
5	6	7	8	9	10	11
12	13	14	15	16	17	18
19	20	21	22	23	24	25
26	27	28	29	30	31	

NOVEMBER

s	m	t	w	t	f	s
						1
2	3	4	5	6	7	8
9	10	11	12	13	14	15
16	17	18	19	20	21	22
23/30	24	25	26	27	28	29

DECEMBER

s	m	t	w	t	f	s
	1	2	3	4	5	6
7	8	9	10	11	12	13
14	15	16	17	18	19	20
21	22	23	24	25	26	27
28	29	30	31			

2007 INTERNATIONAL HOLIDAYS

Following are the observed dates of major (bank-closing) holidays for selected countries in 2007. Islamic observances are subject to adjustment. Holidays for the US, UK, and Canada and major Jewish holidays appear on this calendar's grid pages. Pomegranate is not responsible for errors or omissions in this list. Users of this information should confirm dates with local sources before making international travel or business plans.

ARGENTINA

1 Jan	New Year's Day
2 Apr	Malvinas Islands Memorial
5 Apr	Holy Thursday
6 Apr	Good Friday
8 Apr	Easter
1 May	Labor Day
25 May	Revolution Day
18 Jun	Flag Day
9 Jul	Independence Day
20 Aug	General San Martín Anniversary
15 Oct	Día de la Raza
8 Dec	Immaculate Conception
25 Dec	Christmas

AUSTRALIA

1 Jan	New Year's Day
26 Jan	Australia Day
5 Mar	Labor Day (WA)
12 Mar	Labor Day (Vic) Eight Hours Day (Tas)
19 Mar	Canberra Day (ACT)
6 Apr	Good Friday
7–9 Apr	Easter Holiday
25 Apr	Anzac Day
7 May	Labor Day (Qld) May Day (NT)
4 Jun	Foundation Day (WA)
11 Jun	Queen's Birthday
6 Aug	Bank Holiday (NSW, NT)
1 Oct	Labor Day (NSW, ACT, SA)
25 Dec	Christmas
26 Dec	Boxing Day

BRAZIL

1 Jan	New Year's Day
20 Jan	São Sebastião Day (Rio de Janeiro)
25 Jan	São Paulo Anniversary (São Paulo)
19–20 Feb	Carnival
6 Apr	Good Friday
8 Apr	Easter
21 Apr	Tiradentes Day
1 May	Labor Day
7 Jun	Corpus Christi
9 Jul	State Holiday (São Paulo)
7 Sep	Independence Day
12 Oct	Our Lady of Aparecida
2 Nov	All Souls' Day
15 Nov	Proclamation of the Republic
20 Nov	Zumbi dos Palmares Day (Rio de Janeiro)
25 Dec	Christmas

CHINA (SEE ALSO HONG KONG)

1 Jan	New Year's Day
18–20 Feb	Lunar New Year
8 Mar	Women's Day
1–3 May	Labor Day Holiday
4 May	Youth Day
1 June	Children's Day
1 Aug	Army Day
1–3 Oct	National Holiday

FRANCE

1 Jan	New Year's Day
8–9 Apr	Easter Holiday
1 May	Labor Day
8 May	Armistice Day (WWII)
17 May	Ascension Day
27–28 May	Pentecost/Whitmonday
14 Jul	Bastille Day
15 Aug	Assumption Day
1 Nov	All Saints' Day
11 Nov	Armistice Day (WWI)
25 Dec	Christmas

GERMANY

1 Jan	New Year's Day
6 Jan	Epiphany*
6 Apr	Good Friday
8–9 Apr	Easter Holiday
1 May	Labor Day
17 May	Ascension Day
27–28 May	Pentecost/Whitmonday
7 Jun	Corpus Christi*
15 Aug	Assumption Day*
3 Oct	Unity Day
31 Oct	Reformation Day*
1 Nov	All Saints' Day*
21 Nov	Penance Day*
24–26 Dec	Christmas Holiday
31 Dec	New Year's Eve

*Observed only in some states

HONG KONG

1 Jan	New Year's Day
17–20 Feb	Lunar New Year
5 Apr	Ching Ming Festival
6–9 Apr	Easter Holiday
1 May	Labor Day
24 May	Buddha's Birthday
19 Jun	Tuen Ng Day
2 Jul	SAR Establishment Day
26 Sep	Mid-Autumn Festival
1 Oct	Chinese National Holiday
19 Oct	Chung Yeung Festival
25–26 Dec	Christmas Holiday

INDIA

20 Jan	Muharram (Islamic New Year)
26 Jan	Republic Day
31 Mar	Prophet Muhammad's Birthday Mahavir Jayanthi
6 Apr	Good Friday
2 May	Buddha Purnima
15 Aug	Independence Day
2 Oct	Mahatma Gandhi's Birthday
13 Oct	Ramzan Id (Eid-al-Fitr)
21 Oct	Dussehra
9 Nov	Diwali (Deepavali)
24 Nov	Guru Nanak's Birthday
20 Dec	Bakr-Id (Eid-al-Adha)
25 Dec	Christmas
Additional holidays to be declared	

IRELAND

1 Jan	New Year's Day
17 Mar	St. Patrick's Day
8–9 Apr	Easter Holiday
7 May	May Holiday
4 Jun	June Holiday
6 Aug	August Holiday
29 Oct	October Holiday
25 Dec	Christmas
26 Dec	St. Stephen's Day

ISRAEL

4 Mar	Purim
3 Apr	First day of Pesach
9 Apr	Last day of Pesach
22 Apr	Memorial Day
23 Apr	Independence Day
23 May	Shavuot
24 Jul	Fast of Av
13–14 Sep	Rosh Hashanah
21–22 Sep	Yom Kippur
27 Sep	First day of Sukkot
4–5 Oct	Shemini Atzeret/Simhat Torah

ITALY

1 Jan	New Year's Day
6 Jan	Epiphany
8–9 Apr	Easter Holiday
25 Apr	Liberation Day
1 May	Labor Day
2 Jun	Republic Day
29 Jun	Sts. Peter and Paul (Rome)
15 Aug	Assumption Day
1 Nov	All Saints' Day
8 Dec	Immaculate Conception
25 Dec	Christmas
26 Dec	St. Stephen's Day

2007 INTERNATIONAL HOLIDAYS

JAPAN
1 Jan	New Year's Day
8 Jan	Coming of Age Day
12 Feb	National Foundation Day
21 Mar	Vernal Equinox Holiday
30 Apr	Greenery Day
3 May	Constitution Day
4 May	National Holiday
5 May	Children's Day
16 Jul	Marine Day
17 Sep	Respect for the Aged Day
24 Sep	Autumnal Equinox Holiday
8 Oct	Health and Sports Day
3 Nov	Culture Day
23 Nov	Labor Thanksgiving Day
24 Dec	Emperor's Birthday

KENYA
1 Jan	New Year's Day
6 Apr	Good Friday
8–9 Apr	Easter Holiday
1 May	Labor Day
1 Jun	Madaraka Day
10 Oct	Moi Day
13 Oct	Eid-al-Fitr
20 Oct	Kenyatta Day
12 Dec	Jamhuri Day
25 Dec	Christmas
26 Dec	Boxing Day

MEXICO
1 Jan	New Year's Day
5 Feb	Constitution Day
21 Mar	Benito Juárez's Birthday
5 Apr	Holy Thursday
6 Apr	Good Friday
8 Apr	Easter
1 May	Labor Day
5 May	Battle of Puebla
16 Sep	Independence Day
1 Nov	All Saints' Day
2 Nov	Day of the Dead
20 Nov	Revolution Day
12 Dec	Our Lady of Guadalupe
25 Dec	Christmas

NETHERLANDS
1 Jan	New Year's Day
6 Apr	Good Friday
8–9 Apr	Easter Holiday
30 Apr	Queen's Birthday
4 May	Remembrance Day
5 May	Liberation Day
17 May	Ascension Day
27–28 May	Pentecost/Whitmonday
25–26 Dec	Christmas Holiday

NEW ZEALAND
1–2 Jan	New Year's Holiday
22 Jan	Provincial Anniversary (Wellington)
29 Jan	Provincial Anniversary (Auckland)
6 Feb	Waitangi Day
6 Apr	Good Friday
8–9 Apr	Easter Holiday
25 Apr	Anzac Day
4 Jun	Queen's Birthday
22 Oct	Labor Day
16 Nov	Provincial Anniversary (Canterbury)
25 Dec	Christmas
26 Dec	Boxing Day

NORWAY
1 Jan	New Year's Day
1 Apr	Palm Sunday
5 Apr	Holy Thursday
6 Apr	Good Friday
8–9 Apr	Easter Holiday
1 May	Labor Day
17 May	Ascension Day Constitution Day
27–28 May	Pentecost/Whitmonday
25–26 Dec	Christmas Holiday

PUERTO RICO
1 Jan	New Year's Day
6 Jan	Three Kings Day (Epiphany)
8 Jan	Eugenio María de Hostos' Birthday
22 Mar	Emancipation Day
6 Apr	Good Friday
8 Apr	Easter
16 Apr	José de Diego's Birthday
16 Jul	Luís Muñoz Rivera's Birthday
25 Jul	Constitution Day
27 Jul	José Celso Barbosa's Birthday
8 Oct	Día de la Raza
19 Nov	Discovery of Puerto Rico
25 Dec	Christmas

All US federal holidays also observed.

RUSSIA
1–2 Jan	New Year's Holiday
7 Jan	Orthodox Christmas
23 Feb	Soldiers Day
8 Mar	International Women's Day
8 Apr	Orthodox Easter
1–2 May	Spring and Labor Day
9 May	Victory Day
12 Jun	Independence Day
7 Nov	Reconciliation Day
12 Dec	Constitution Day

SINGAPORE
1 Jan	New Year's Day
2 Jan	Hari Raya Haji (Eid-al-Adha)
18–20 Feb	Lunar New Year
6 Apr	Good Friday
8 Apr	Easter
1 May	Labor Day
31 May	Vesak Day (Buddha's Birthday)
9 Aug	National Day
13 Oct	Hari Raya Puasa (Eid-al-Fitr)
9 Nov	Deepavali
20 Dec	Hari Raya Haji (Eid-al-Adha)
25 Dec	Christmas

SOUTH AFRICA
1 Jan	New Year's Day
21 Mar	Human Rights Day
6 Apr	Good Friday
8 Apr	Easter
9 Apr	Family Day
27 Apr	Freedom Day
1 May	Labor Day
16 Jun	Youth Day
9 Aug	National Women's Day
24 Sep	Heritage Day
17 Dec	Day of Reconciliation
25 Dec	Christmas
26 Dec	Day of Goodwill

SPAIN
1 Jan	New Year's Day
6 Jan	Epiphany
19 Mar	St. Joseph's Day
5 Apr	Holy Thursday
6 Apr	Good Friday
8 Apr	Easter
1 May	Labor Day
25 Jul	St. James the Apostle Day
15 Aug	Assumption Day
12 Oct	National Holiday
1 Nov	All Saints' Day
6 Dec	Constitution Day
8 Dec	Immaculate Conception
25 Dec	Christmas

SWITZERLAND
1 Jan	New Year's Day
2 Jan	Berchtold's Day
6 Apr	Good Friday
8–9 Apr	Easter Holiday
17 May	Ascension Day
27–28 May	Pentecost/Whitmonday
1 Aug	National Day
25 Dec	Christmas
26 Dec	St. Stephen's Day

THAILAND
1 Jan	New Year's Day
2 Mar	Makha Bucha Day
6 Apr	Chakri Day
13–15 Apr	Songkran Festival
1 May	Labor Day Visakha Bucha Day (Buddha's Birthday)
7 May	Coronation Day
31 Jul	Buddhist Lent Day
13 Aug	Queen's Birthday
23 Oct	Chulalongkorn Day
5 Dec	King's Birthday
10 Dec	Constitution Day
31 Dec	New Year's Eve

- From the United States, dial 011 (international access code), country code, city code, and local telephone number.
- Numbers listed alongside country names are country codes.
- Numbers listed alongside city names are city codes; an asterisk (*) means that no city code is needed.
- Numbers in parentheses indicate hourly differences from Pacific Standard Time. A range of numbers indicates a country with more than one time zone.
- Canada, US territories, and many Caribbean nations follow the North American Numbering Plan (dial 1 + 3-digit area code + local number) and are not listed here.

ALBANIA 355	(+9)	
TIRANA 4		
ALGERIA 213	(+9)	
ALGIERS 2		
ARGENTINA 54	(+5)	
BUENOS AIRES 11		
CÓRDOBA 351		
SANTA FÉ 342		
ARMENIA 374	(+12)	
YEREVAN 10		
ARUBA 297	(+4)	
ALL CITIES 8		
AUSTRALIA 61	(+16–18)	
ADELAIDE 8		
BRISBANE 7		
CANBERRA 2		
MELBOURNE 3		
PERTH 8		
SYDNEY 2		
AUSTRIA 43	(+9)	
SALZBURG 662		
VIENNA 1		
BANGLADESH 880	(+14)	
CHITTAGONG 31		
DHAKA 2		
BELGIUM 32	(+9)	
ANTWERP 3		
BRUSSELS 2		
GHENT 9		
BOLIVIA 591	(+4)	
LA PAZ 2		
SANTA CRUZ 3		
BOSNIA-HERZEGOVINA .. 387	(+9)	
SARAJEVO 33		
BRAZIL 55	(+3–6)	
BRASÍLIA 61		
RIO DE JANEIRO 21		
SALVADOR 71		
SÃO PAULO 11		
BULGARIA 359	(+10)	
SOFIA 2		
CAMBODIA 855	(+15)	
PHNOM PENH 23		
CAMEROON 237*	(+9)	
CENTRAL AFRICAN REPUBLIC 236*	(+9)	
CHILE 56	(+4)	
CONCEPCIÓN 41		
SANTIAGO 2		
VALPARAÍSO 32		

CHINA 86	(+16)	
BEIJING 10		
CANTON (GUANGZHOU) 20		
FUZHOU 591		
SHANGHAI 21		
COLOMBIA 57	(+3)	
BOGOTÁ 1		
CALI 2		
MEDELLÍN 4		
CONGO 242*	(+9)	
CONGO, DEMOCRATIC		
REPUBLIC OF 243	(+9–10)	
KINSHASA 1		
COSTA RICA 506*	(+2)	
CROATIA 385	(+9)	
DUBROVNIK 20		
ZAGREB 1		
CUBA 53	(+3)	
GUANTÁNAMO BAY NAVAL BASE (FROM US ONLY) 99		
HAVANA 7		
CYPRUS 357	(+10)	
NICOSIA 22		
CZECH REPUBLIC 420	(+9)	
PRAGUE 2		
DENMARK 45*	(+9)	
ECUADOR 593	(+3)	
GUAYAQUIL 4		
QUITO 2		
EGYPT 20	(+10)	
ALEXANDRIA 3		
CAIRO 2		
EL SALVADOR 503*	(+2)	
ESTONIA 372	(+10)	
TALLINN 6		
ETHIOPIA 251	(+11)	
ADDIS ABABA 1		
FIJI 679*	(+20)	
FINLAND 358	(+10)	
HELSINKI 9		
FRANCE 33	(+9)	
BORDEAUX 5		
MARSEILLE 491		
NICE 4		
PARIS 1		
REIMS 3		
ROUEN 2		
TOULOUSE 5		
FRENCH ANTILLES 590*	(+4)	
FRENCH POLYNESIA 689*	(-1--2)	
(MOOREA AND TAHITI)		
GEORGIA 995	(+12)	
TBILISI 32		
GERMANY 49	(+9)	
BERLIN 30		
FRANKFURT 69		
HAMBURG 40		
MUNICH 89		
GIBRALTAR 350*	(+9)	
GREECE 30	(+10)	
ATHENS 1		
IRÁKLION (CRETE) 81		
GUATEMALA 502	(+2)	
GUATEMALA CITY 2		

HAITI 509*	(+3)	
HONDURAS 504*	(+2)	
HONG KONG 852*	(+16)	
HUNGARY 36	(+9)	
BUDAPEST 1		
DEBRECEN 52		
ICELAND 354*	(+8)	
INDIA 91	(+13.5)	
BANGALORE 80		
BOMBAY (MUMBAI) 22		
CALCUTTA 33		
MADRAS 44		
NEW DELHI 11		
INDONESIA 62	(+15–17)	
JAKARTA 21		
IRAN 98	(+11.5)	
ESFAHAN 311		
SHIRAZ 711		
TEHRAN 211		
IRAQ 964	(+11)	
BAGHDAD 1		
BASRA 40		
KIRKUK 50		
MOSUL 60		
IRELAND 353	(+8)	
CORK 21		
DUBLIN 1		
ISRAEL 972	(+10)	
HAIFA 4		
JERUSALEM 2		
TEL AVIV 3		
ITALY 39	(+9)	
FLORENCE 055		
GENOA 010		
MILAN 02		
NAPLES 081		
ROME 06		
VENICE 041		
IVORY COAST 225*	(+8)	
JAPAN 81	(+17)	
KYOTO 75		
TOKYO 3		
YOKOHAMA 45		
JORDAN 962	(+10)	
AMMAN 6		
KARAK 3		
KENYA 254	(+11)	
MOMBASA 11		
NAIROBI 2		
N. KOREA 850	(+17)	
S. KOREA 82	(+17)	
KWANGJU 62		
PUSAN 51		
SEOUL 2		
TAEGU 53		
KUWAIT 965*	(+11)	
LAOS 856	(+15)	
VIENTIANE 21		
LATVIA 371	(+10)	
RIGA 2		
LEBANON 961	(+10)	
BEIRUT 1		
LIBERIA 231*	(+8)	

INTERNATIONAL CALLING CODES/TIME DIFFERENCES

LIBYA 218   (+10)
  TRIPOLI 21
LIECHTENSTEIN .... 423*   (+9)
LITHUANIA 370   (+10)
  KAUNAS 37
LUXEMBOURG .... 352*   (+9)
MACAU .... 853*   (+16)
MACEDONIA 389   (+9)
MALAYSIA 60   (+16)
  IPOH 5
  KUALA LUMPUR 3
MEXICO 52   (+0–2)
  ACAPULCO 744
  CABO SAN LUCAS 624
  CANCÚN 998
  CIUDAD JUÁREZ 656
  ENSENADA 646
  GUADALAJARA 33
  LA PAZ 612
  MAZATLÁN 669
  MEXICALI 686
  MEXICO CITY 55
  MONTERREY 81
  TIJUANA 664
  VERACRUZ 229
MONACO .... 377*   (+9)
MOROCCO 212   (+8)
  MARRAKECH 44
  RABAT 37
MOZAMBIQUE 258   (+10)
  MAPUTO 1
MYANMAR 95   (+14.5)
  RANGOON (YANGON) 1
NAMIBIA 264   (+9)
  WINDHOEK 61
NEPAL 977   (+14)
  KATHMANDU 1
NETHERLANDS 31   (+9)
  AMSTERDAM 20
  THE HAGUE (DEN HAAG) 70
  ROTTERDAM 10
NETHERLANDS ANTILLES.. 599   (+4)
  CURAÇAO 9
  ST. MAARTEN 5
NEW ZEALAND 64   (+20–21)
  AUCKLAND 9
  CHRISTCHURCH 3
  WELLINGTON 4
NICARAGUA 505   (+2)
  LEÓN 311
  MANAGUA 2
NIGERIA 234   (+9)
  LAGOS 1
NORWAY .... 47*   (+9)
PAKISTAN 92   (+13)
  ISLAMABAD 51
  KARACHI 21
  LAHORE 42
PANAMA .... 507*   (+3)
PARAGUAY 595   (+4)
  ASUNCIÓN 21
  CONCEPCIÓN 31

PERU 51   (+3)
  AREQUIPA 54
  LIMA 1
PHILIPPINES 63   (+16)
  BACOLOD 34
  CEBU CITY 32
  DAVAO 82
  ILOILO CITY 33
  MANILA 2
POLAND 48   (+9)
  GDANSK 58
  KRAKOW 12
  WARSAW 22
PORTUGAL 351   (+8)
  LISBON 21
ROMANIA 40   (+10)
  BUCHAREST 21
RUSSIA 7   (+10–20)
  MOSCOW 095
  ST. PETERSBURG 812
SAUDI ARABIA 966   (+11)
  JEDDAH 2
  MECCA (MAKKAH) 2
  RIYADH 1
SENEGAL .... 221*   (+8)
SERBIA AND MONTENEGRO 381   (+9)
  BELGRADE 11
  CETINJE 86
SINGAPORE .... 65*   (+16)
SLOVAKIA 421   (+9)
  BRATISLAVA 2
SLOVENIA 386   (+9)
  LJUBLJANA 1
  MARIBOR 2
SOUTH AFRICA 27   (+10)
  BLOEMFONTEIN 51
  CAPE TOWN 21
  DURBAN 31
  JOHANNESBURG 11
  PRETORIA 12
SPAIN 34   (+9)
  BARCELONA 93
  GRANADA 958
  MADRID 91
  PALMA DE MALLORCA 971
  PAMPLONA 948
  SEVILLE 95
  VALENCIA 96
SRI LANKA 94   (+14)
  COLUMBO CENTRAL 1
SURINAME .... 597*   (+5)
SWEDEN 46   (+9)
  MALMO 40
  STOCKHOLM 8
SWITZERLAND 41   (+9)
  BASEL 61
  BERNE 31
  GENEVA 22
  LAUSANNE 21
  LUCERNE 41
  ZÜRICH 1
SYRIA 963   (+10)
  DAMASCUS 11

TAIWAN 886   (+16)
  KAO-HSIUNG 7
  TAINAN 6
  TAIPEI 2
TANZANIA 255   (+11)
  DAR ES SALAAM 22
  TANGA 27
THAILAND 66   (+15)
  BANGKOK 2
  CHANTHABURI 39
TUNISIA 216   (+9)
  BIZERTE 2
  TUNIS 1
TURKEY 90   (+10)
  ANKARA 312
  ISTANBUL
    ASIAN 216
    EUROPEAN 212
UGANDA 256   (+11)
  ENTEBBE 42
  KAMPALA 41
UKRAINE 380   (+10)
  DONETSK 62(2)
  KIEV 44
  LVOV 32(2)
UNITED ARAB EMIRATES.. 971   (+12)
  ABU DHABI 2
  AJMAN 6
  AL AIN 3
  FUJAIRAH 9
UNITED KINGDOM 44   (+8)
  BELFAST 28
  BIRMINGHAM 121
  CARDIFF 29
  EDINBURGH 131
  GLASGOW 141
  LIVERPOOL 151
  LONDON 20
  MANCHESTER 161
  SOUTHAMPTON 23
URUGUAY 598   (+5)
  CANELONES 332
  MERCEDES 532
  MONTEVIDEO 2
VATICAN CITY 39   (+9)
  ALL POINTS 6
VENEZUELA 58   (+4)
  CARACAS 212
  MARACAIBO 261
  MARACAY 243
  VALENCIA 241
VIETNAM 84   (+15)
  HANOI 4
  HO CHI MINH CITY 8
YEMEN 967   (+11)
  ADEN 2
  SANA'A 1
  ZABID 3
ZAMBIA 260   (+10)
  LUSAKA 1
ZIMBABWE 263   (+10)
  HARARE 4

NOTES

personal information

name _____

address _____

city _____ state _____ _____ zip _____

phone _____

cell/pgr _____ fax _____

e-mail _____

in case of emergency, please notify:

name _____

address _____

city _____ state _____ zip _____

phone _____

physician's name _____

physician's phone _____

health insurance company _____

plan number _____

allergies _____

other _____

driver's license number _____

car insurance company _____

policy number _____